51 PIANO PIECES

from the modern repertoire

REPRESENTING COMPOSERS
OF THIRTEEN NATIONALITIES

G. SCHIRMER   New York / London

Ed. 1672

INDEX BY COMPOSERS

38977

CONTENTS
BY NATIONALITIES OF COMPOSERS

Nocturnal Tangier

(Triakontameron, No. 1)

Leopold Godowsky

Andante espressivo ♩=76-88

38977

The White Peacock

Charles T. Griffes

4

Languidamente e molto rubato

Piano

una corda

molto dim. e rit.

June, 1915

Impromptu

John Alden Carpenter
July, 1913

38977

Chanty
from "Poems of the Sea"

Ernest Bloch

(in the style of a folk-song)

Nº 1. "SPOON RIVER"

(For Edgar Lee Masters, poet of pioneers)

American folk-dance, heard played by a fiddler at a country dance at Bradford, Illinois, in **1857**, by Capt. Charles H. Robinson

and set for piano by

PERCY ALDRIDGE GRAINGER

Set, March 10, 1919,
New York City, and
Jan. 29-30, 1922,
White Plains, N.Y.

20

Bass hugely to the fore

small hands

The accents very heavy

louden

small hands

38977

Written out in train, Canadian
Rockies, March 24, 1922

Little Suite

Roy Harris

1. Bells

S. P. = Sustaining Pedal

88977

2. Sad News

una corda

3. Children at Play

4. Slumber

Sourwood Mountain

Arthur Farwell. Op. 78, No. 3

With animation and humor ♩=112

Piano

Grotesque Dance

Lukas Foss

Tempo Iº

Darkey playing, on harmonica, to his little dancing, cut-the-pigeon-wing pickaninnies in the shadow of the cabin-door, at the close of day.

Alley Tunes

III

The Harmonica-Player

David W. Guion

With marked swing and rhythm ♩ = 132

Piano

38977

The Moon Rises

Adagio ♩ = 42

Ernst Křenek, Op. 83, No. 4

Bagatelle

Béla Bartók

*If there is no *rit.* or *acc.* in front of the metronome mark, the change of tempo is sudden.

**) Execution: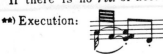

à Emmanuel Chabrier

Le Chant des Bruyères*
The Song of the Heath

Vincent d'Indy

*From "Poème des Montagnes" (Poem of the Mountains), Op. 15

(BROUILLARD)
Un poco più vivace

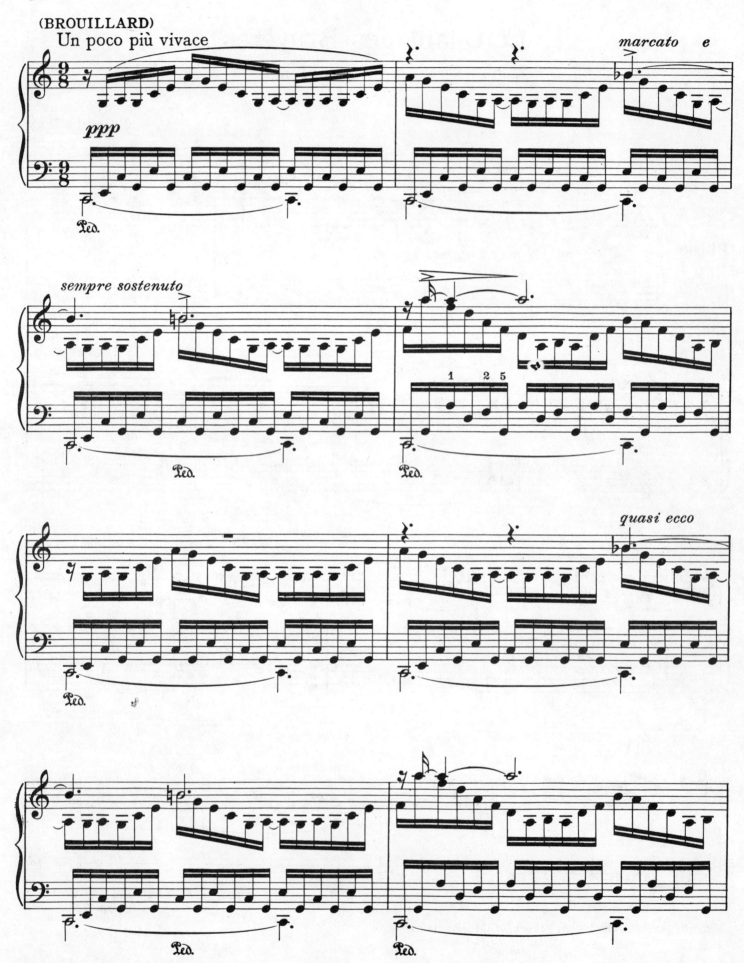

(LA BIEN-AIMÉE)
Lento

(LOINTAIN)
Andante tranquillo come I°

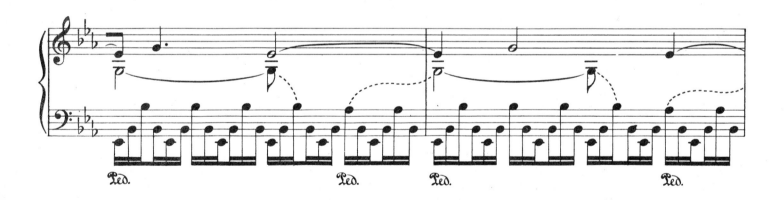

à Louis Diémer

Laufenburg

Vincent d' Indy, Op. 17, No. 3*

*From "Helvetia", a set of three waltzes, each bearing the name of a town in northern Switzerland.

38977

38977

38977

à Gabriel Fauré

Aarau

Vincent d' Indy, Op. 17, No. 1*

Piano

*From "Helvetia", a set of three waltzes, each bearing the name of a town in northern Switzerland.

38977

à Mademoiselle Marguerite Lamoureux

Habanera

Emmanuel Chabrier

Valse romantique

Edited by Carl Deis

Claude Debussy

Rêverie

As played by
Harold Bauer

Claude Debussy

38977

Berceuse

Gabriel Fauré, Op. 56, No. 1

Impromptu

Edited by Carl Deis

Gabriel Fauré, Op. 31, No. 2

Allegro molto

Piano

leggero

poco a poco cresc.

to Conrad Satie

Gymnopédie
(a Greek ceremonial dance)

Erik Satie

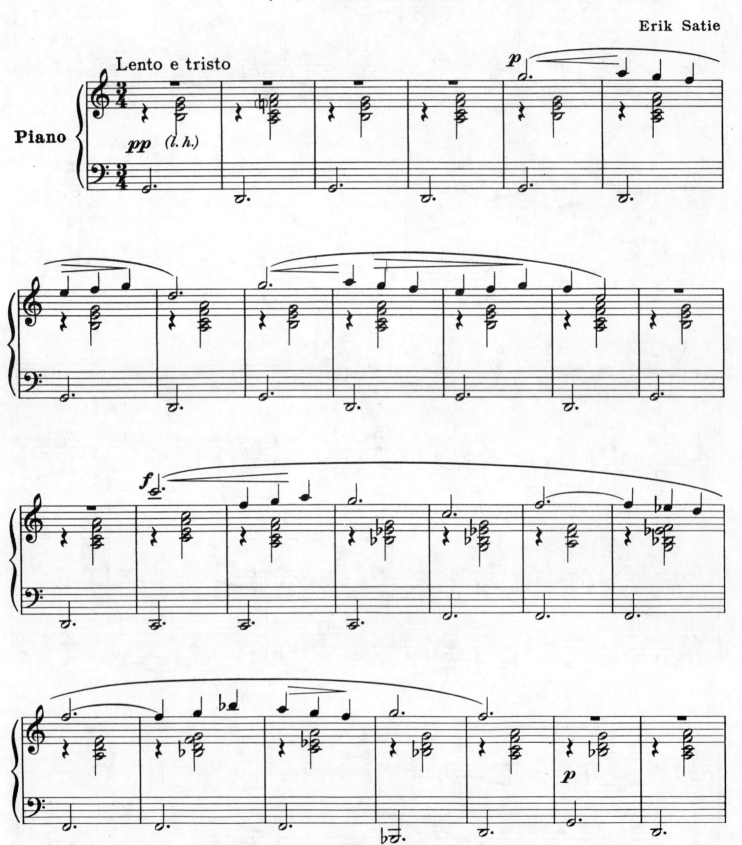

à mon cher Maître Gabriel Fauré

Jeux d'Eau

Dieu fluvial riant de l'eau qui le chatouille.

Henri de Régnier

Edited and revised by
Rafael Joseffy

Maurice Ravel

88977

il canto un poco marcato

rapido

38977

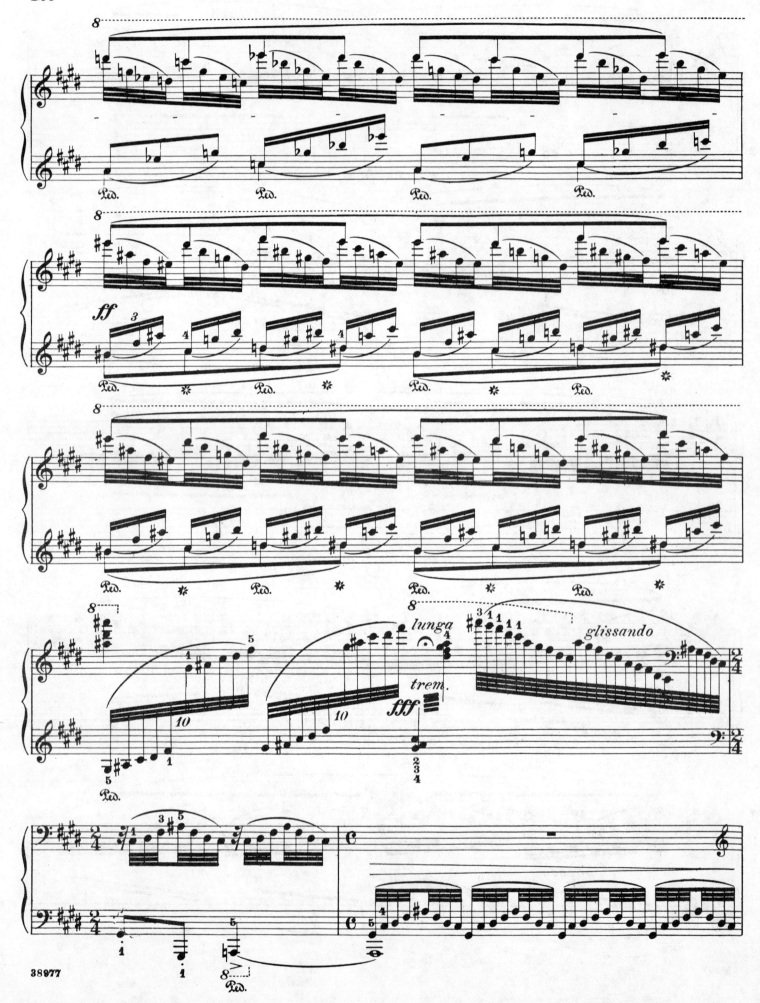

38977

tre corde

rall. leggermente

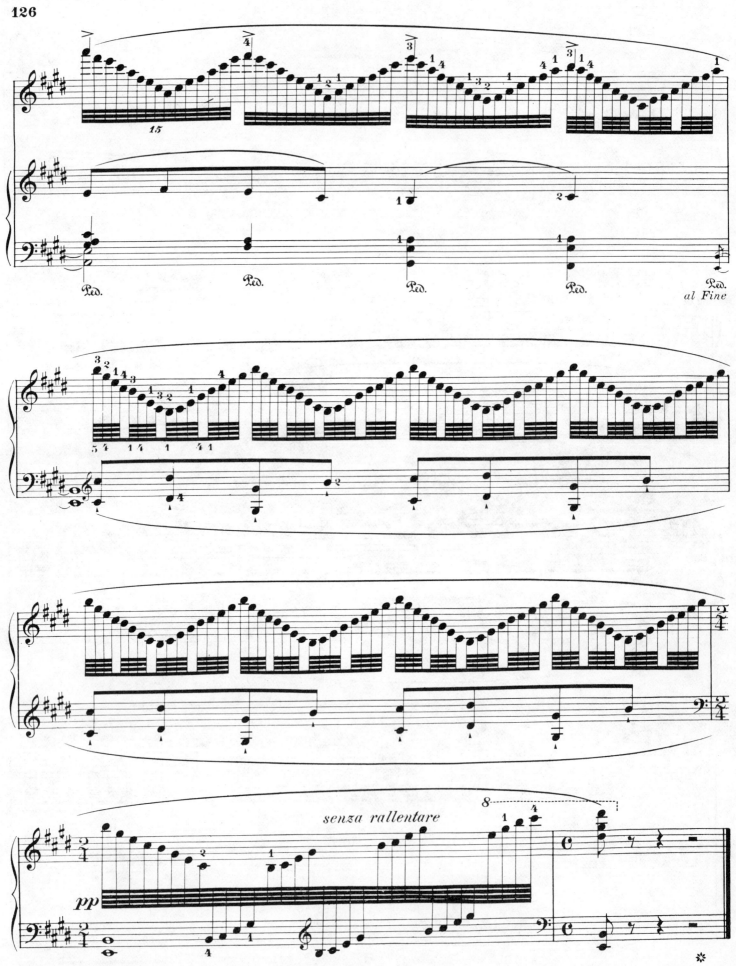

Pavane
Pour une Infante défunte

Maurice Ravel

Notturno

Ottorino Respighi

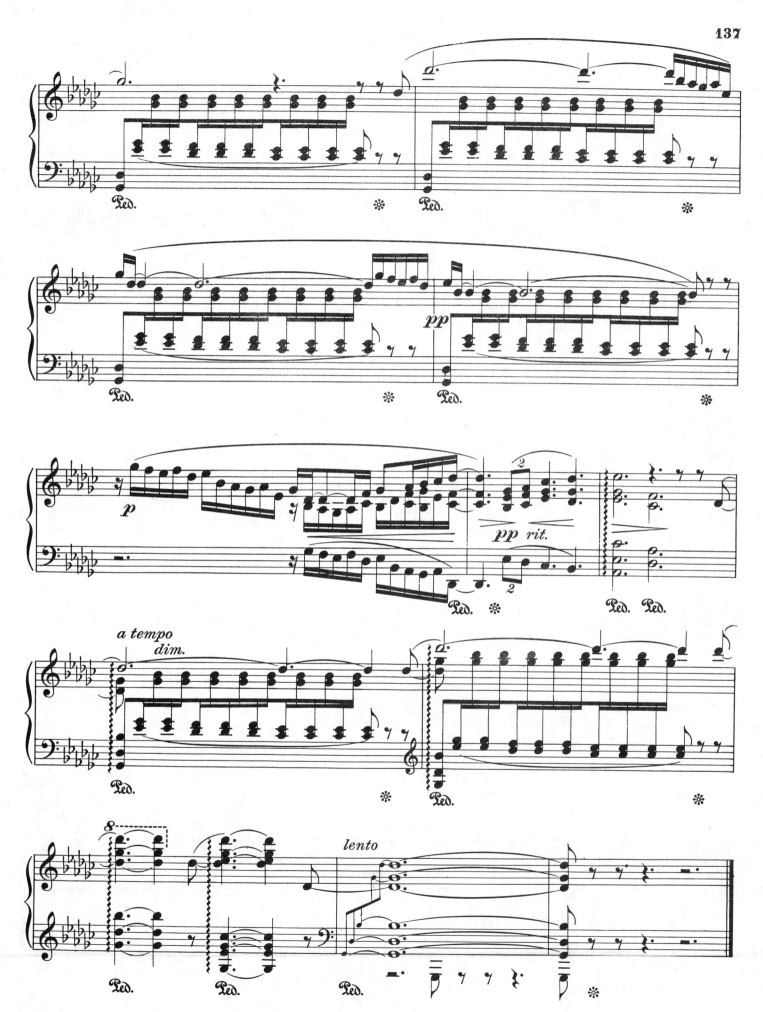

38977

Omaggio a C. Collodi *

Pinocchio

Renato Bellini

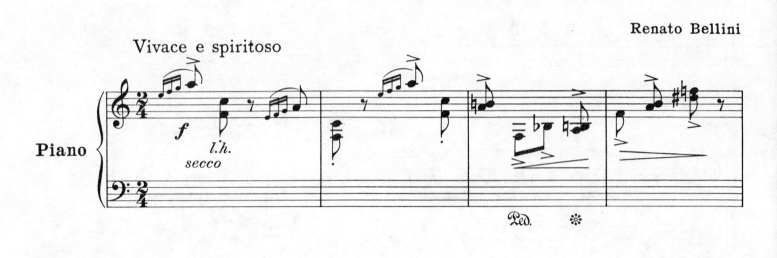

* Author of the original *Pinocchio*

Andante mosso *(con espressione e rubando)*

Vivo

con pedale

Vivace e spiritoso

Orientale

Isaac Albéniz

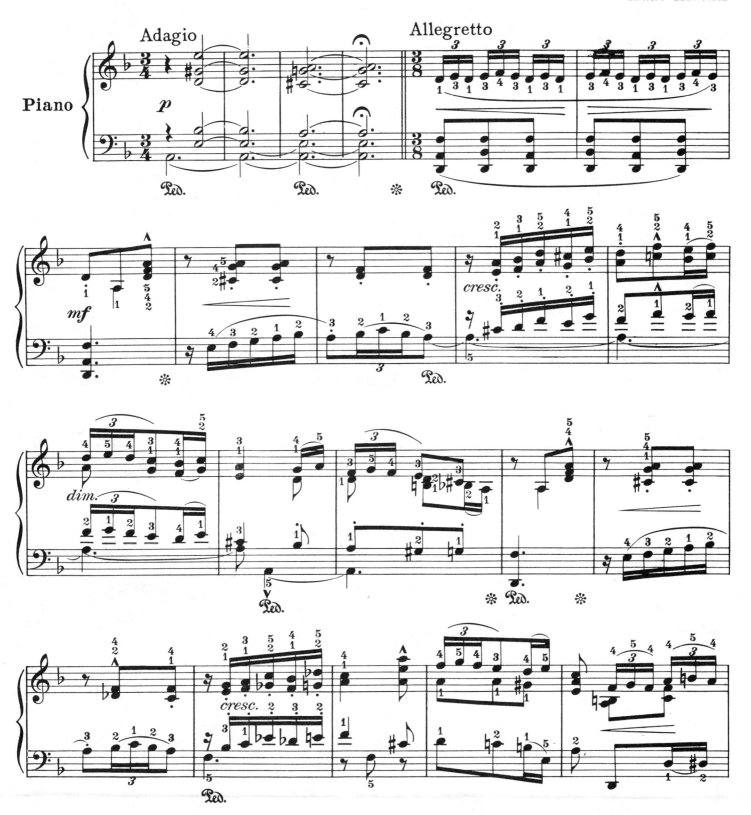

Tango

Edited by Carl Deis

Isaac Albéniz, Op. 164, No. 2

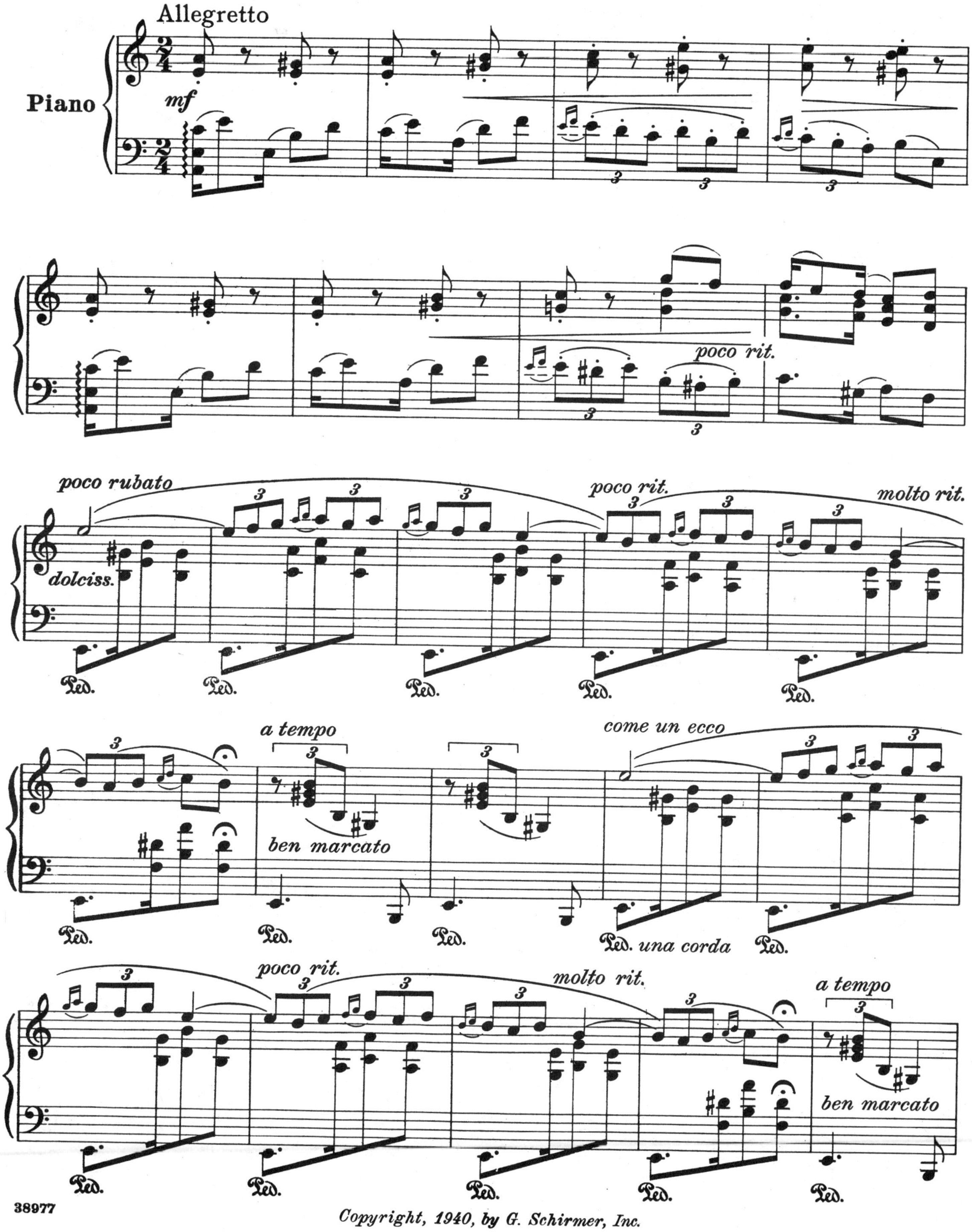

Poco meno mosso

38977

to D. Murillo

Rondalla Aragonesa

Enrique Granados

Serenata Andaluza

Edited by Carl Deis

Manuel de Falla

An einsamer Quelle
By the Lonely Spring

Richard Strauss, Op. 9, No. 2

38977

Träumerei
Revery

Edited and fingered by
Louis Oesterle

Richard Strauss. Op. 9, № 4

Piano

Die Pedalzeichen sind sehr genau zu beobachten!
Close attention should be paid to the pedal marks.

38977

38977

Humoresque

Max Reger, Op. 79ª, No. 2

Vivacissimo
(Äusserst lebhaft)

Piano

Gavot

Ludwig Thuille

Valse
Ma mie qui danse

Béla Bartók, Op. 6, No. 14

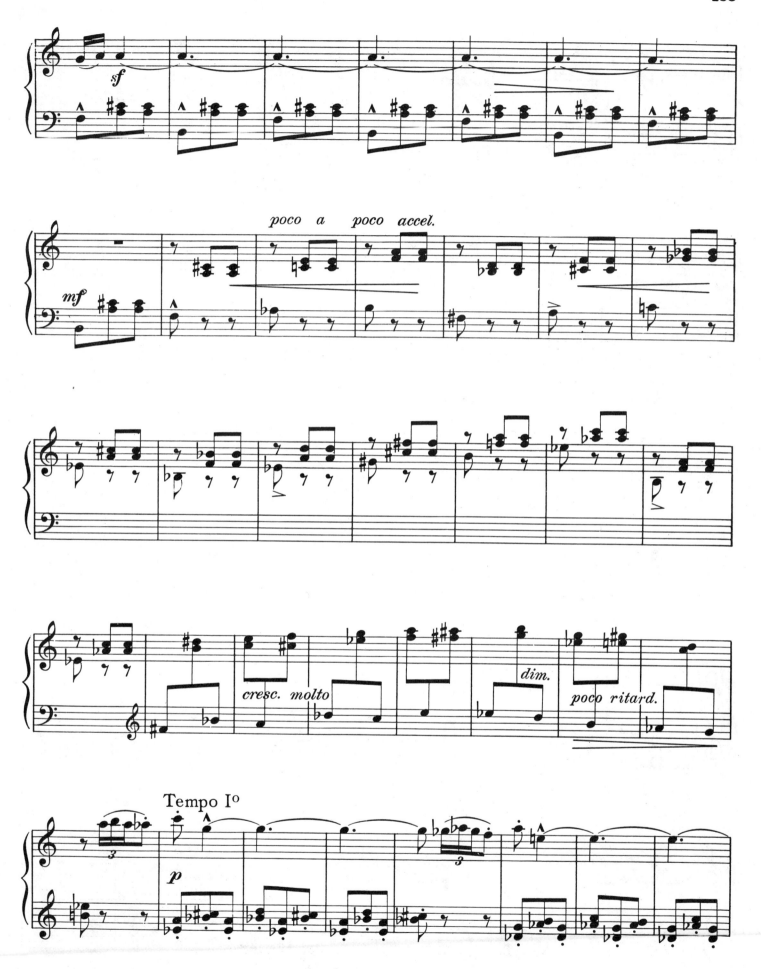

Bear Dance

Béla Bartók

38977

Romance

Jean Sibelius, Op. 24, No. 9

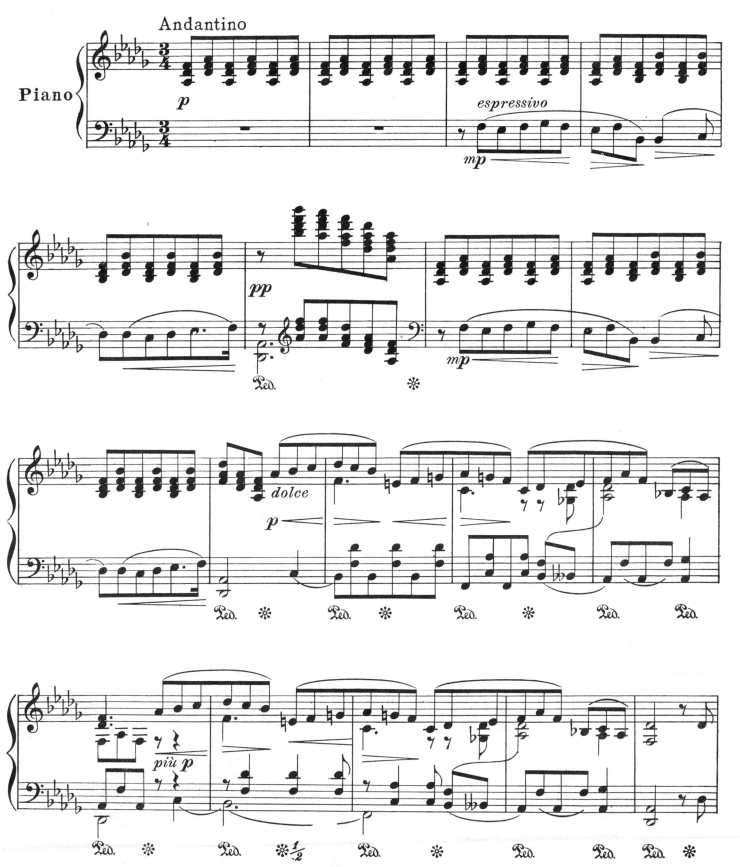

38977

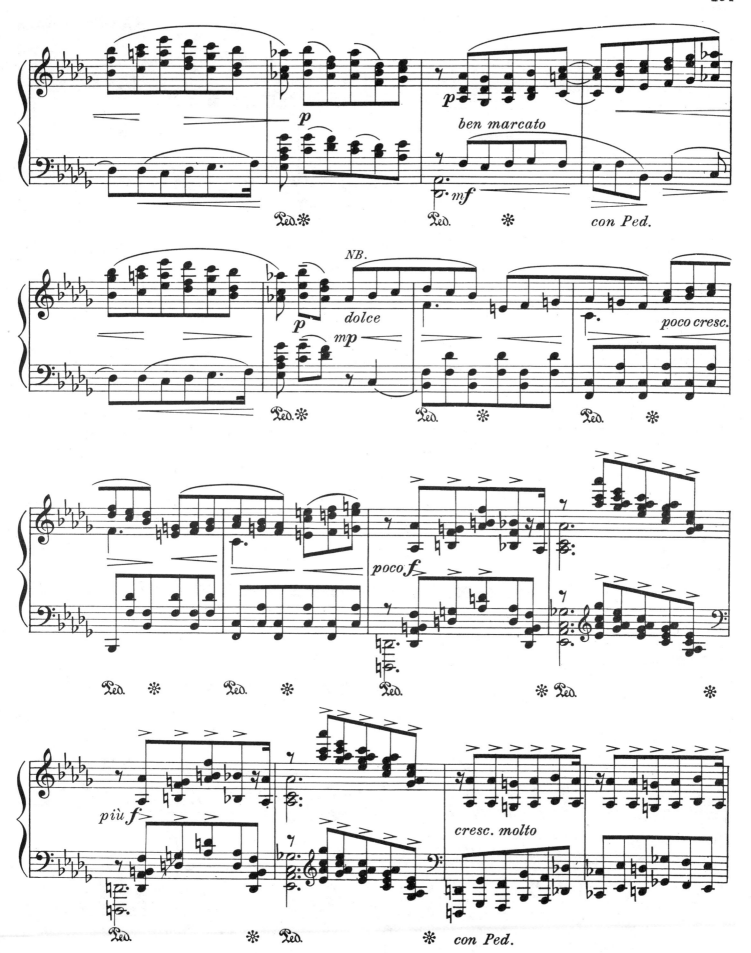

NB. If desired, a cut may be made from here to the point on the last page indicated by the sign ⊕.

38977

Spring Night

Selim Palmgren, Op. 22, No. 8

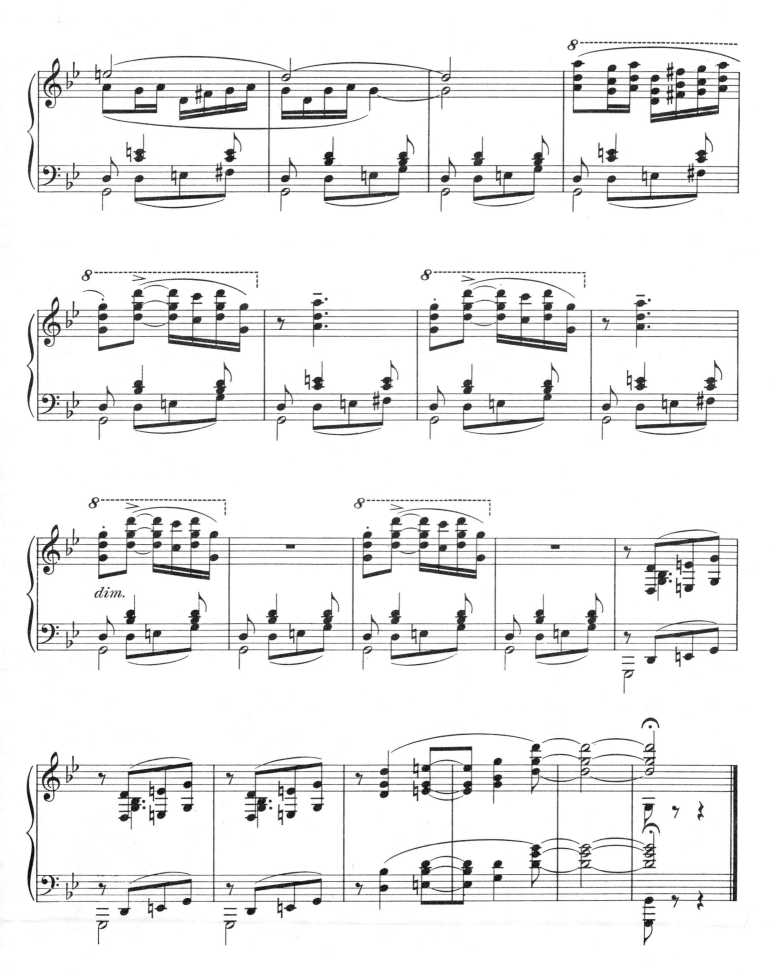

Impression

Zdenko Fibich, Op. 44, No. 32

38977

Étude

Karol Szymanowski, Op. 4, No. 3

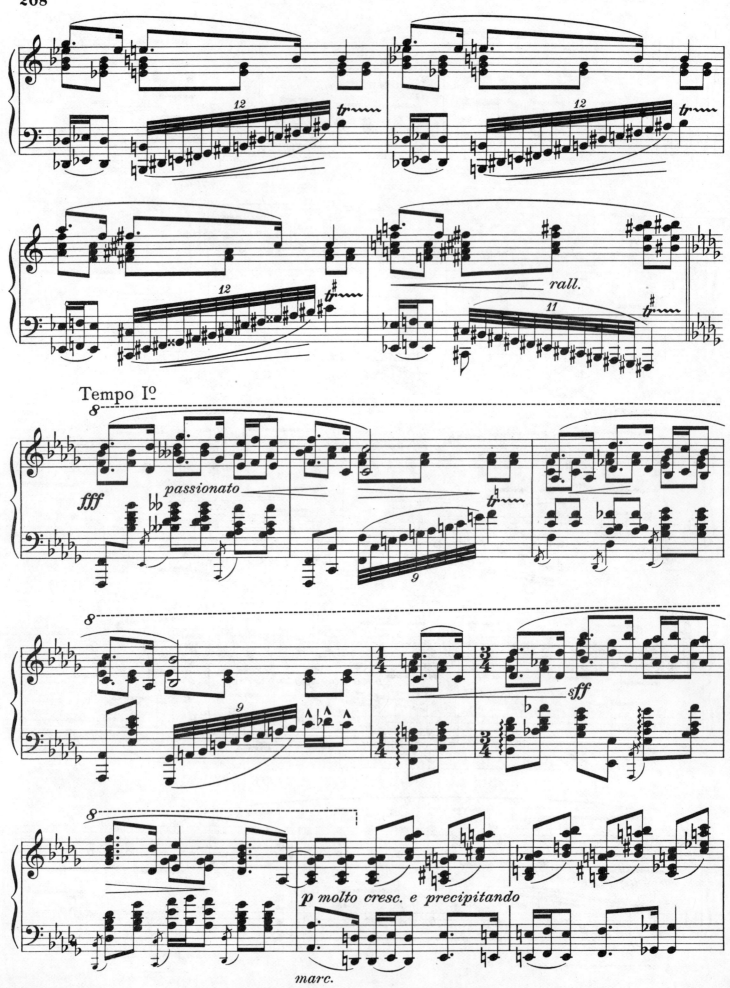

Poëme

Alexander Scriabin, Op. 69, No. 1

Mazurka

Alexander Scriabin, Op. 25, No. 4

Étude

Igor Stravinsky, Op. 7, No. 2

Allegro brillante ♩. = 76

Piano

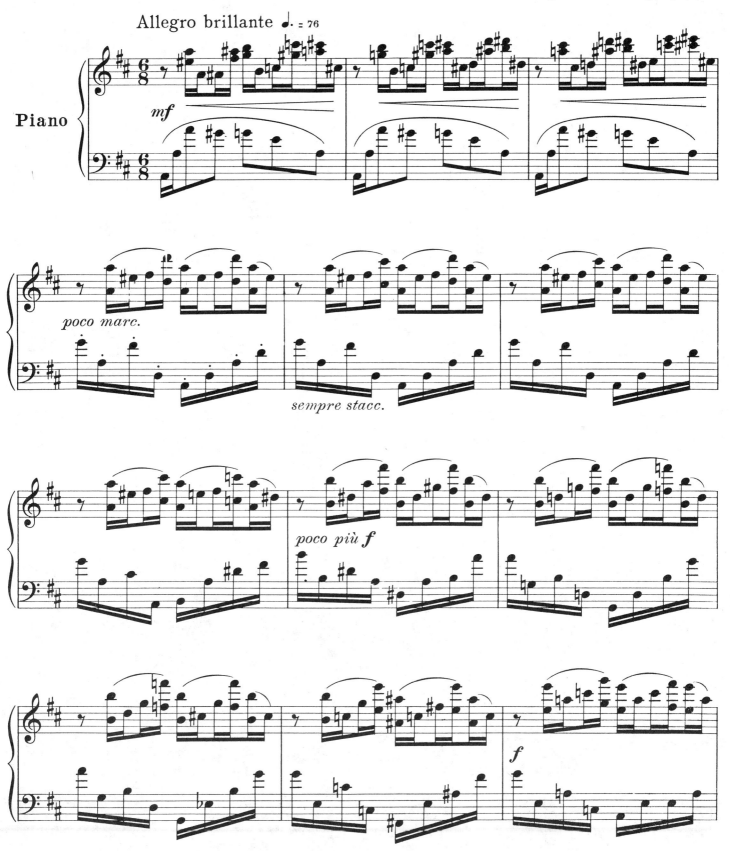

38977

Les Démons s'amusent

Vladimir Rebikov

Vision Fugitive

Specially edited by
The Composer

Serge Prokofieff. Op. 22, No. 16
1915

A Monsieur Boris Zaharoff

Gavotte

Specially edited by
The Composer

Serge Prokofieff. Op. 12, No. 2
1908

38977

A M. Basile Moroleff

Marche

Specially edited by
The Composer

Serge Prokofieff. Op. 12, No. 1
1906 (1913)

236

38977

à *Monsieur A. Siloti*

Prelude in E flat

Fingered by Carl Deis

Sergei Rachmaninoff, Op. 23, No. 6

A Monsieur A. Arensky

Élégie

Edited and fingered by
Andor Pintér

S. Rachmaninoff. Op. **3**, № **1**

38977

Copyright, 1913, by G. Schirmer, Inc.

38977

Più vivo

a tempo

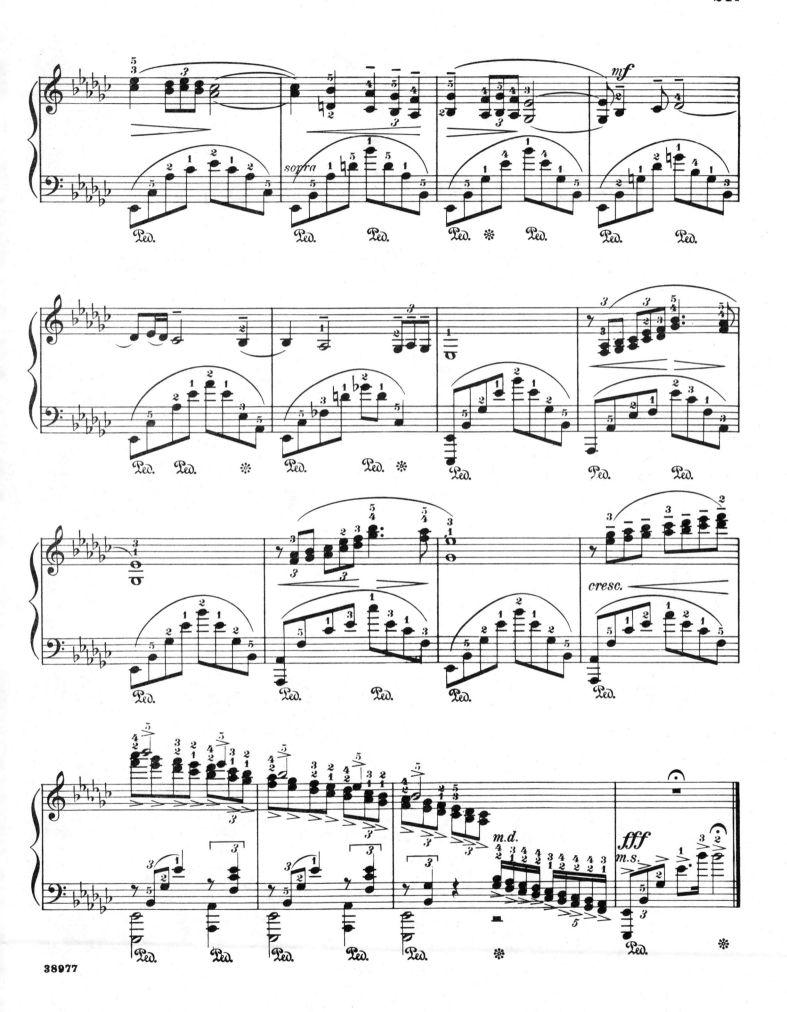

Polka
from the ballet "L'Age d'or"

Dmitri Shostakovitch, Op. 22

Prelude

from "Ten Preludes"

Carlos Chávez

*In the case of a slight accent, the composer has used the following sign: ⨼. This is, let us say, half as strong as the regular accent, ⨼. The dash, ⨼, has the usual meaning of giving full duration to the sound.

Marcha do Pequeno Polegar

Tom Thumb's March

Octavio Pint

To Fernando Waymann

La Hiladora
The Spinner

A Study for Piano

Enrique Soro